My First Bible Stories

Retold by Nick Ellsworth

Illustrated by
Roger Langton and
Sara Sliwinska

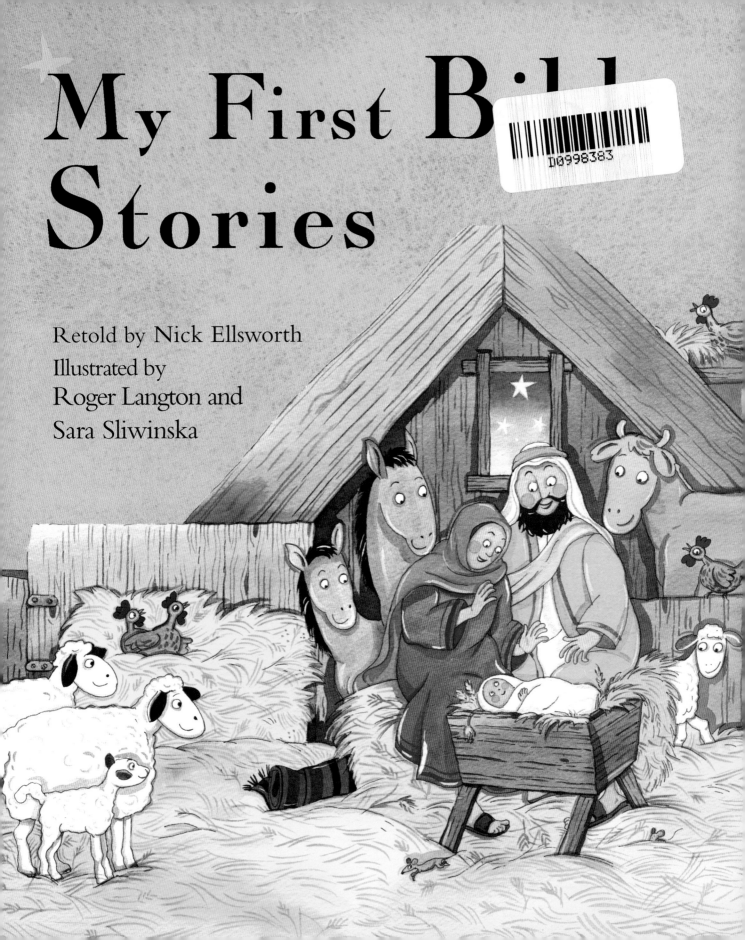

D0998383

The Old Testament

The New Testament

THE OLD TESTAMENT

In The Beginning

GENESIS 1-2

In the beginning there was God. Then God created Earth. But to begin with, Earth was as dark as night. So God said, "Let there be light!" So He made the Sun. Now there was day to go with night.

Then God made the sky and, underneath the sky, He gathered together huge amounts of water to make the seas.

And in-between the seas He made rocks and mountains and soil. Then He made flowers and forests of trees which could grow in the soil.

Then God made fish that could live in the seas and birds that could fly in the sky and animals that could live on the land.

He then made the first man, whom He called Adam. God thought Adam might be lonely all by himself, so He made the first woman, whom He called Eve.

It had taken God six long days to make everything in the world so , on the seventh day, He rested. He decided from then on, every seventh day should be a day of rest.

And this special day of rest He called the Sabbath.

Adam and Eve

GENESIS 2-3

God gave Adam and Eve a beautiful garden to live in, which He called the Garden of Eden. He filled it with the loveliest flowers and plants. There were rivers Adam and Eve could drink from, and trees bearing the most delicious fruit. It was truly paradise.

In the centre of the garden, God planted a special tree.
"This is the Tree of Knowledge of Good and Evil," He told them.
"Do not eat the fruit that grows on it. If you do, you will die."

Adam and Eve lived happily in the garden for many years and made sure that they never ate the fruit that grew on the special tree.

14

But, one day, a slimy snake slithered up to Eve and hissed, "You really should taste the apples that grow on the Tree of Knowledge. They really are the most delicious fruit in the garden."

Eve was a little frightened.

"But God said we'd die if we tasted the fruit from that tree," she said.

"You won't die!" mocked the snake. "God said that because He knows if you were to eat the fruit, you would become as wise as He, and He wouldn't want that to happen, would He?"

Eve thought this made sense. So she walked slowly to the Tree of Knowledge, picked off the juciest, ripest apple she could see and took a big bite out of it. And, when she saw Adam a little later, she shared the fruit with him.

When God realized what they had done, He was angry. "You have disobeyed me," He said. "You must now leave this beautiful garden. From this day on, you must work hard to grow your own food in the rough and thorny ground that lies beyond here. And when you grow old, you will die."

So Adam and Eve left the Garden of Eden. Their lives became much harder, and they struggled to grow enough to eat in the hot, harsh lands outside the Garden.

For the rest of their days, they regretted the time when they disobeyed God by eating the fruit that grew on the Tree of Knowledge.

Cain and Abel

Adam and Eve had two sons. One was called Cain, the other, Abel. Cain worked in the fields growing crops while his brother Abel looked after the sheep on the hills.

They both grew up loving God and tried to please Him in any way they could.

Once, Cain offered some of his freshly cut crops to God, while Abel offered Him one of his new born lambs. God was pleased with Abel's lamb but did not want Cain's crops, thinking they were not worthy of Him.

Cain was jealous that God had accepted Abel's offering, but not his own. One day he suggested to his brother that they should go for a walk together. While they were out, Cain killed his brother.

When Cain returned home, God asked him where Abel was.

"I don't know," replied Cain. "Am I my brother's keeper?"

But God knew what he had done and said, "Your brother's blood cries out to me from the ground. You will be punished for your evil. You will spend the rest of your life wandering the earth, and you will find no rest."

"But I will be killed by the first person who sees me," cried Cain.

"You will not," said God. "I will put a mark on you that tells people that if they dare to kill you, I will take seven lives in revenge."

So Cain collected his few belongings and left his home forever.

Noah's Ark

GENESIS 6-9

God was angry. He saw that most people on Earth were not obeying him, so He decided to flood the whole world and drown everyone in it.

But there was one man He decided to save. This man's name was Noah. God knew that Noah was a good man and wanted to save him from the flood.

"You and your family must build a great Ark," God told him. "In it, you will gather together two of every animal on Earth. Do this and you will be saved."

Noah and his family set to work. They cut down the tallest trees and used them to make the frame of the Ark. Then they covered the frame with rough planks of wood and put tar on the inside so that water couldn't get in.

They all worked very hard for many months. Finally, it was finished.

Noah then gathered together two of every single creature on Earth, just as God had told him to do. The animals lined up and slowly began to troop into the Ark. There were so many of them, it took a very long time. Everyone helped to load enough food and water to last them for months. Once Noah and his family had joined the animals on board, Noah shut the huge doors behind them.

Then, the rains began.

25

It rained for forty days and forty nights. Soon, the whole Earth was covered with water and became one big sea. The only things left alive on Earth were the people and animals inside the Ark.

For months and months, the Ark tossed around on the sea. Noah peered through the windows every day, hoping to see signs of dry land, but he saw only water.

One day he sent out a raven to look for dry land, but the raven didn't return.

Then he sent out a dove to look for dry land, but the dove didn't return, either.

Noah sent out a second dove. When it returned with an olive leaf in its beak, Noah knew this was a sign that the waters were going down, and dry land wasn't too far away.

He sent out the dove once more and this time it didn't return. Noah now knew beyond doubt that the flood had almost disappeared. He looked out of a window and was overjoyed to see dry land on the horizon.

Gathering his family together, Noah told them the news they had waited so long to hear. Then they sailed happily towards the shore.

After he had made sure all the animals
left the Ark safely, Noah got down
on one knee and thanked
God for keeping his
family safe.

"I promise," said God, "however angry I become, I will never again destroy what I have created."

Then He put a beautiful rainbow in the sky.
"Whenever I see a rainbow," said God, "it will remind me to keep my promise. And when you see a rainbow, think of my promise and be certain that I will keep it."

The Tall Tower

GENESIS 11

After the great flood, Noah's sons had children, then those children had children, and on it went. Noah's descendants filled every country in the world, and they all spoke one language.

They were learning about things too; they learned that if you baked clay it would become very hard and, from this, you could make strong bricks. With strong bricks, you could build houses and buildings.

One day, someone in a place called Babel had an idea.
"Let's build a tower and make it the tallest tower anyone has ever seen!" he said excitedly. "We will become famous and everyone will envy us."

Work began on the tower. But God, who had been watching them, became sad.
"These people are becoming as selfish and vain as the people I punished with the great flood," He thought. "They have learnt nothing. I must teach them a lesson."

So God made everyone speak in different languages. Because they couldn't understand each other, the tower couldn't be finished. So everyone had to go and live in the part of the world where their language was spoken so they would be understood.

Abraham

GENESIS 12-13, 15, 18, 21

Abraham was one of Noah's descendants. He was a wealthy man and lived with his wife, Sarah, in a place called Haran. Although Abraham and Sarah had a happy life together, their one great sadness was that they had no children.

One day, God spoke to Abraham.
"I want you to take everything you own and go and live in the land of Canaan. There, I will make you the father of a great nation." Abraham loved God, so he did as God asked. He gathered together all his sheep and goats, and made the long journey to Canaan with Sarah. His nephew Lot, and Lot's wife, also went with him.

At first, there was plenty of grass and water for Abraham's animals but, as the years passed and his flock grew bigger, there wasn't enough to feed them all.
"Let me go and live further down the valley," said Lot. "There will be much more grass and water down there."
Abraham would miss Lot, but knew it was the right thing to do.

Some years later, Abraham saw three men passing by close to his tent. He invited them in to share a meal with him. When they had finished eating, one of the men told Abraham that he had a message for him, from God.

"You and Sarah are going to have a baby," the man smiled.

"But Sarah is far too old to have a baby!" Abraham exclaimed.

To his amazement, some months later Sarah gave birth to a baby boy. They called him Isaac. It was then that Abraham remembered God's words from many years ago: "I will make you the father of a great nation."

Abraham was very proud that his son Isaac would be the first child of that nation.

Isaac and Rebecca

GENESIS 24

Isaac grew up to be a fine young man. After Sarah's death, Abraham decided it was time for his son to have a wife. He wanted to find a girl from his home country for Isaac. For this difficult task, he sent his most trusted servant.

The journey was long and tiring, so the servant decided to stop and rest outside the city walls. As he rested, he saw some girls who had come to fill their water jugs from a nearby well.
"I will ask one of them for water," thought the servant. "And if she brings water for my camel, too, I know she will make a fine wife for Isaac."

He picked out the girl who looked the kindest and asked her for a cup of water. To his delight, the girl filled his cup, then ran off to bring water for his camel.

The servant fell to his knees and thanked God for leading him to such a kind, lovely girl.

He was so taken with her, he asked her if she would take him to see her parents.

"They would be delighted to meet you," replied the girl, whose name was Rebecca.

She took him to her house where he was welcomed, and offered food and shelter for the night.

As night fell, the servant began to tell Rebecca's parents of Abraham's wish to find a wife for his son. He told them that he thought Rebecca would make the perfect wife for Isaac. The more the servant talked, the more Rebecca's parents came to understand that God had intended their daughter to be with Isaac.

They agreed to the marriage at once.

There was much joy in the house that night.

Early the next morning, Abraham's servant started his long journey back to Canaan. Rebecca and her parents had agreed that she should go with him.

It was evening when Rebecca and the servant arrived in Canaan. Isaac rushed back from the fields where he was working and stared at the beautiful girl standing in front of him.
He fell in love with her immediately.

A happy Isaac and Rebecca were married shortly after.

Joseph and His Brothers

GENESIS 37, 39-47

Isaac's son, Jacob, was a wealthy man who lived with his family in Canaan. He had twelve sons whom he loved dearly, but Joseph was the son he loved the most.

One day, Jacob gave Joseph a beautiful coat to wear. The other sons were so jealous they wanted to hurt their brother.

"Let's kill him!" one of the brothers said. "We could tell father that a wild animal has eaten him."

"Why don't we just throw him down a pit?" another brother suggested.

As they were talking together, some merchants passed by. The brothers decided to sell Joseph to the merchants as a slave. Then they smeared his beautiful new coat with goat's blood and took it to their father. When Jacob saw the blood-soaked coat, he thought his beloved Joseph was dead.

The merchants journeyed to Egypt where they sold Joseph to Potiphar, the captain of the King's guard. Joseph worked hard and was soon put in charge of the other servants. But Potiphar's wife didn't like him, and told her husband Joseph had been rude to her. Potiphar was so angry he had Joseph thrown into prison.

In prison, Joseph found he was clever at explaining people's dreams to them. News of Joseph's talent spread far and wide, even reaching the King's ears. He sent for Joseph and asked him to help him understand a dream which had been worrying him. It was about seven plump cows who came out of the river Nile and ate the grass, followed by seven thin cows who ate the plump ones.

"Your dream means that Egypt will have good harvests for seven years, after which there will be seven years of bad harvests," Joseph told the King. "You must be very careful or many of your people will go hungry."

The King was so pleased with Joseph, he put him in charge of all the food supplies in Egypt. Joseph cleverly stored away a lot of corn during the first seven years when the crops were good, so that everyone would have enough to eat during the next seven years when the crops were bad.

Meanwhile, in Canaan, Jacob and his family were growing short of food. Jacob told his sons to go to Egypt, to buy corn there. But he didn't want them to take his youngest son, Benjamin, with them.

The man they had to buy food from in Egypt was their brother, Joseph. Although Joseph knew who they were, his brothers didn't recognize him. Joseph noticed that Benjamin, whom he missed the most, was not with them.

"I will sell you food," Joseph told them sternly. "But only if you return home and come back with your brother Benjamin."

When the brothers returned home, they told their father that they must return to Egypt with Benjamin. Jacob was terrified. He didn't want any harm to come to his youngest son.

"We must return with him, father," said the brothers. "We will starve to death unless we can buy some corn."

Jacob had no choice and finally agreed to let Benjamin go with them.

Joseph was overjoyed to see Benjamin again, but he wanted to know if his brothers had changed before he told them who he was. After he'd sold them the food they wanted, he secretly hid his silver drinking cup in the sack of corn that Benjamin was carrying.

When the missing cup was discovered by Joseph's soldiers, Joseph ordered Benjamin to stay in Egypt and work as a servant. When the brothers heard this, they got down on their knees.

"Please sir," they begged. "It would kill our father if we don't take our youngest brother back with us. Spare him. Take one of us instead!"

When Joseph heard these desperate pleas, he realized just how much his brothers had changed.

"Do not worry," he smiled. "I would never make a brother of mine unhappy. Do you not recognize me? I am Joseph."

His brothers couldn't believe what they heard. They stood up and hugged Joseph, with tears in their eyes.

"Joseph!" they cried. "Our long lost brother. We thought we'd never see you again! How can you ever forgive us for what we did to you all those years ago?"

But Joseph did forgive them, and told them to bring Jacob to Egypt, where they all lived happily as one big family again.

Moses in the Bulrushes

EXODUS 1-2

Many years after Joseph died, a new King came to power in Egypt. He hated the Hebrews and made them work as slaves, doing all the dirtiest and hardest jobs that the Egyptians didn't want to do. The King made them work very long hours and they were whipped and beaten if they tried to rest.

As there were more and more Hebrews being born in Egypt every year, the King became afraid that they would one day turn against their Egyptian masters and take over the whole country. So he ordered his soldiers to kill every Hebrew boy as soon as he was born. One clever Hebrew mother managed to hide her baby until he was three months old. After that, he was getting too big to hide, so she had to think of another way to protect him. His mother had named him Moses.

She took him down to the water's edge of the great River Nile and set him afloat in a small basket made of reeds. She was sad to see him float away, but knew it was the only way to save him. Her daughter, Miriam, followed the little basket as it floated away.

Some distance down the river, an Egyptian Princess was bathing in its clear waters. She noticed the basket as it bobbed its way towards her. When she looked inside, she was surprised to see a small baby.

"This must be a poor Hebrew child," she said to one of her hand-maidens. The Princess felt so sorry for the little baby she decided to keep him.

Miriam, who had been hiding in the bulrushes, had an idea. She boldly approached the Princess.
"Your Highness," she said. "I know of a very caring Hebrew woman who could nurse this baby for you."

"Bring her to me!" ordered the Princess. Miriam ran off and returned with her mother who was secretly delighted to see her baby son again. She agreed that she would nurse Moses until he was older, then he would be taken to live with the Princess at the Palace.

A few years later, Moses went and lived with the Princess and she cared for him as if he was her own son.

From that day on, Moses was treated as an Egyptian Prince. When he became a young man it made him angry to see his people treated as slaves and he wondered how long he could keep his anger hidden. He never forgot that, deep down inside, he was still a Hebrew.

The Burning Bush

EXODUS 2-4

One day, Moses's anger was put to the test when he saw an Egyptian savagely whipping a Hebrew slave; he couldn't contain his feelings any longer and attacked the Egyptian, killing him where he stood.

When the King of Egypt heard what Moses had done, he tried to have Moses killed. Fortunately, Moses managed to escape into the desert before the King's soldiers found him.

He lived in the desert for many years but never forgot the Hebrew slaves in Egypt who were still suffering.

One day, while he was tending sheep, Moses saw a bush that seemed to be on fire. When he got closer, he saw that flames were leaping from the bush but, strangely, the bush was not being burned.

Then, he heard God's voice speaking to him.
"You must go back to Egypt and ask the King to release the Hebrew slaves," said God. "Then you will lead the Hebrews to a land where they will have plenty of food and water."

The Plagues of Egypt

EXODUS 7-12

Moses returned to Egypt and asked the King to set all the Hebrew free. But the King refused. An unhappy Moses asked for God's help. In order to change the King's mind, God promised he would cause strange and terrible things to happen in Egypt:

First the river turned red so no one could drink the water.

Then frogs came from the river and invaded the Egyptian houses.

Then swarms of terrible flies did the same.

Moses asked the King again if he would free the slaves.

Once again, the King refused.

Then all the animals began to die,

and terrible sores broke out all over the Egyptians' bodies.

But the King still would not set the Hebrews free.

Then violent storms ruined the crops,

and armies of locusts ate the few crops that were left.
But the King still would not free the slaves.

Then, one night every eldest child of every single family died.

However, God told Moses that if the Hebrews killed a lamb and put a little of its blood on the doorframes, then roasted and ate the lamb with bread and herbs, death would pass over them.
From that day on, this feast was known as the Passover. It celebrates the time when death passed over the Hebrew houses in Egypt.

The Parting of the Red Sea

EXODUS 14

After the deaths of the Egyptian children, the King had no choice but to let the slaves go free.

Moses gathered all the Hebrews together and led them out of Egypt. But the King became angry and ordered his soldiers to follow and kill every one of them.

When Moses heard the soldiers behind him, he realized there was no escape. The Red Sea lay straight ahead of them. Moses lifted his staff and commanded the sea to part, allowing the Hebrews to walk safely across.

When the last Hebrew reached the other side, the sea rushed back, drowning all the Egyptian soldiers who were following.

61

Moses in the Desert

EXODUS 15-17

After many weeks of walking through the barren desert, the Hebrews were tired and hungry.

"We were better off in Egypt," they said. "At least we had food and water there."

Moses was very worried but God spoke to him and comforted him. "Tell the people I will give them meat every evening and bread every morning, except on the seventh day, which will be My day of rest. That day will be called the Sabbath."

That evening, a huge flock of birds surrounded the tents where they slept. There were so many birds, they were easy to catch. At supper, the Hebrews filled their empty stomachs with the meat of the birds.

The next morning, the people looked out of their tents and saw that the ground was covered in seeds. The people gathered up as much of the seed as they could, ground it into flour and made it into bread.

"God has sent you this bread," Moses explained. "It is called Manna."

63

But soon the people were complaining again.

"We have no water to drink!" they grumbled. "How can we live without water?"

Moses turned to God for help, saying to him, "These people are dying of thirst and I have no water for them."

"Take your staff and strike the first rock you see," commanded God.

Moses followed God's command. He walked up to the first rock he saw and struck it with his staff. As soon as he did so, an enormous fountain of fresh water gushed out. Now that they had water as well as food, the people were happy at last.

God's Ten Laws

EXODUS 19-20

God told Moses to lead his people to the foot of Mount Sinai where something important would happen. They arrived at the foot of the mountain three months after they had left Egypt.

Moses asked the people to make camp and to wait for him. Then he slowly started to climb to the top of Mount Sinai where he knew God wanted to speak to him alone.

Moses was gone for many days. At the foot of the mountain, the Hebrew people were getting restless.

"God has left us," they said to each other. "We must build ourselves a new god to worship." So they collected all the gold in the camp, melted it down and made a golden calf to which they began to pray.

Moses came down from the mountain carrying two stone tablets that had the laws of God written on them. But when he saw the people worshiping the golden calf, he became angry and smashed the golden calf into little pieces.

"These are the laws of the only true God!" he said, pointing to the stone tablets. "Study them well and abide by them."

These were God's ten laws:

I am your one and true God. You must have no gods other than me.

You must not make false idols and worship them.

Always say My name with respect.

You must work for six days and rest on the seventh.

Always treat your mother and father with respect.

Do not kill any other human being.

People who are married must always be faithful to each other.

Do not steal.

It is wrong to tell lies.

Do not be envious of what other people have.

Jericho Falls

JOSHUA 1-6

Now that the Hebrew people had food and water, they were able to survive in the desert. After forty years, their great leader, Moses, died. Their new leader was a man called Joshua.

"As I was with Moses, so will I be with you. Be strong and courageous, for I will be with you wherever you go," God told Joshua. Joshua prepared his people to cross the River Jordan. On the other side lay Canaan, the land that God had always promised them.

But the great city of Jericho, with its massive walls, stood in their way. When the people of Jericho heard that the Hebrew soldiers were nearby, they quickly filled in any cracks and holes in the walls so that the city was impossible to enter.

God spoke again to Joshua.

"The city of Jericho will be yours if you follow these commands. You and your soldiers must march around the city walls for six days. Six priests must march in front of you, blowing their horns."

"On the seventh day, when the priests and soldiers have marched around the walls seven times, the Hebrew soldiers and people must give one huge shout. Then Jericho's massive walls will fall down."

Joshua followed God's orders exactly. And on the seventh day, when the Hebrew people shouted as loud as they could, the enormous walls of Jericho came crashing down. The soldiers rushed in, and soon, the city was taken.

This was the Hebrew people's first victory in the 'promised land'. Over the years, they settled in Canaan and become a very strong nation.

Samson

JUDGES 13-16

After many years of living in Canaan, the Hebrew people or, as they were later known, the Israelites, began worshipping false gods again. To punish them, God made them slaves of a people called the Philistines.

One day, an Israelite woman gave birth to a baby boy called Samson. An angel had appeared to Samson's mother before his birth. "Do not cut your child's hair," said the angel. "His long hair will give him strength, and show that he is destined to serve God."

When Samson grew up, he did indeed become very strong. Once, when a lion came roaring towards him, Samson killed it with his bare hands.

Over the years, Samson used his great strength against the Philistines and became their greatest enemy. He once killed a thousand Philistine soldiers, using only the jawbone of a donkey as a weapon.

When Samson fell in love with a girl called Delilah, the Philistines
promised her money if she could discover the secret of his
strength. Because he loved her, Samson told Delilah his secret.

"My strength lies in my long hair," he said. "If it were cut, I would be no stronger than any other man."

That night, Delilah allowed a Philistine in to where Samson was sleeping. The Philistine quickly cut off all of Samson's hair. When he woke, Samson realized that he had lost all of his strength. Then the Philistine soldiers burst in and put him into prison. But time passed and Samson's hair started to grow back again.

One day, the Philistines held a feast in one of their biggest Temples. They strung up Samson between two large pillars. Many people flocked to the Temple to laugh and jeer at him.
"Look at him!" they mocked. "Not so strong now!"
The crowd's teasing made Samson so angry he prayed to God to give him all his strength back. Then he pushed against the two pillars. The whole Temple collapsed under Samson's mighty strength. Samson was killed, but so, too, were the thousands of Philistines who had been inside the Temple with him.

It was Samson's last show of strength to the enemies of Israel.

Ruth

RUTH 1-4

There was once a woman called Naomi who lived with her husband and two sons in Bethlehem. When famine struck, Naomi and her family went to live in a far off country called Moab. Her sons married girls called Orpah and Ruth.

Over the next ten years, Naomi's husband, and both sons died. Now an old woman, Naomi decided to make the long journey back to Bethlehem. Orpah and Ruth wanted to go with her, but Naomi begged them to stay and find new husbands in the country they knew.

Orpah agreed, but brave Ruth decided to take care of Naomi and to follow her wherever she went.

When they reached Bethlehem the harvest was beginning. Having little food, Ruth went into the fields every day hoping to pick up the ears of corn that had been missed. The farmer who owned the fields was a man called Boaz. He had heard how good Ruth had been to Naomi, and offered her all the water and corn she needed.

When Ruth told Naomi of Boaz's kindness, Naomi said, "This shows that God still cares for us. Even though our loved ones are dead, He has sent Boaz to help us."

Boaz started to care for Ruth, and asked her to marry him. Ruth happily agreed. Soon after, she gave birth to a baby boy. Naomi loved the boy very much and thanked God for giving her such a beautiful grandson.

David and Goliath

1 SAMUEL 16-17

Ruth's great grandson, David, worked on his father's farm. His job was to look after the sheep that grazed on the hills. He was a fearless boy who often had to defend his sheep against wild animals such as wolves and bears. He became an expert with a slingshot, which he fired stones with, to drive the wild animals away.

For years, King Saul of the Israelites had been fighting the Philistines. Down in the valley below David, a huge battle was about to take place. On one side of the valley lay the Israelite soldiers and, on the other, the mighty Philistine army.

One day, David's father asked him to take some food to his brothers who were soldiers in the Israelite army. As David got nearer, he could see the two great armies lined up opposite each other.

Suddenly, a giant of a man stepped out from the line of Philistine soldiers.

"My name is Goliath," he shouted to the Israelites. "I am the fiercest fighter in the world! No one can beat me! I challenge one of you to fight me! If you win, you win the battle for your whole army!"

The Israelite soldiers shrank back in fear. None of them dared to fight Goliath alone. Then David stepped forward.

"I'll fight you," he said. "I'm not afraid of you."

Goliath threw his head back and roared with laughter.

"Don't be silly, little boy. I will kill you in an instant."

"No, you won't," replied David. "I have God on my side."

King Saul tried to persuade David not to fight, but David's reply was simple and brave:

"Do not worry, my King. God will help me."

Saul gave David his armour, but it was far too heavy for him to wear.

81

"I just need my slingshot and my faith in God," said David. Then the giant and the boy walked out to fight each other. David bent down and picked up five smooth stones from the river bed. All of a sudden, Goliath charged at him with a huge roar. David carefully loaded his slingshot with one of the stones, took aim and fired it at the giant. The stone hit Goliath right between the eyes, and buried deep in his forehead. He was stopped in an instant and fell dead at David's feet.

The Philistines could not believe that their hero, Goliath, was dead. The Israelites cheered their new hero, David, and chased the Philistine soldiers all the way back to their city gates. David was his country's saviour. He became famous throughout the land and eventually, when he grew up, became King of Israel.

King David

2 SAMUEL 5-11

Many years later, when David did become King of Israel, he had many other battles to fight; he fought against people who still supported the old King, Saul, and against the Philistines who longed to return to Israel.

David had always wanted to capture Jerusalem. In time, he succeeded, and made it God's city.

David was a much loved King, but he had weaknesses that made God sad. Once, he fell in love with a woman called Bathsheba, but she was already married to a soldier in David's army. David wanted Bathsheba so much he arranged to have her husband killed.

Afterwards, he felt so guilty he spent many days praying for God's forgiveness.

God did forgive him and promised David he would remain as King, but David was disappointed when God gave the task of building a new Temple to David's son, Solomon instead of him.

Later, David married Bathsheba. He remained a strong leader but it was a time of many problems for Israel.

Absalom

2 SAMUEL 14-18

Of all David's children, his son, Absalom, was the most loved. He was a handsome young man with thick, dark hair. He was also very proud and, because people loved him, he began to believe that he should be King.

Absalom asked his father, King David, to allow him to go to Hebron where he could worship God. But, when he got to Hebron, Absalom decided he was going to fight his father for the crown and raised a huge army.

King David was distraught when he heard of his son's plans, and sent out thousands of his own soldiers out to meet Absalom's army.

There was a huge battle. David still loved his son, and told his army to show mercy to Absalom should they catch him. When Absalom's long hair became tangled in the branches of a tree, one of David's generals, Joab, disobeyed David's command and ordered three spears to be plunged into Absalom's chest, killing him immediately.

When David heard of his son's death, he wept. "I wish I had died instead of you," he cried. "Oh Absalom, my son, my son!"

King Solomon

1 KINGS 1-3

When King David became very old and weak, he took to ruling Israel from his bed. He knew that death was near, and wanted to be sure that the throne would pass into a safe pair of hands.

Years before, he had promised God that his son, Solomon, would be the new King when he died. But another of David's sons, Adonijah, grew ambitious and wanted the throne for himself.

When eventually Solomon did become King, Adonijah was afraid that Solomon might punish him for wanting the crown for himself. But Solomon told Adonijah that he would not harm him as long as he remained a good man.

Most of all, Solomon wanted to be wise. When God appeared to him in a dream, Solomon asked Him for the gift of wisdom. God promised He would make Solomon wise and, because Solomon asked for nothing but wisdom, God also promised him great wealth and a long life.

One day, two women came to see King Solomon. They had a baby with them, and each woman said that the baby belonged to her. They wanted Solomon to decide who was the real mother.

"Bring me a sword," said Solomon. "I will cut the baby in half. In this way, you can share this child," he told the women.

One of the women agreed to this at once, but the other cried out, "No! I would rather see my baby brought up by another woman than see my child killed."

Solomon now knew for sure that this woman was the baby's true mother. Only the real mother would allow the child to be brought up by someone else rather than see it die.

"Take your baby," he said, handing the infant to the woman, "and go in peace."

God had been true to His word. He had made Solomon a great leader, and all the people of Israel marvelled at his wisdom.

Solomon's Temple

1 KINGS 5-8

In the fourth year of his reign, King Solomon decided to build a huge Temple from only the finest materials. The Temple was made up of two large rooms: an outer room and an inner room. The best cedar wood to line the walls was given by King Hiram of Tyre; this was carved into the shapes of trees, flowers and birds. The outer room contained an altar and ten gold lamp stands. The inner room was windowless. In this room stood the box holding God's laws. In both rooms, everything was covered in gold. Outside the Temple were courtyards, where people could pray and offer gifts to God.

Thousands of men worked on the Temple and, by the time it was finished, it had taken seven years to build. Solomon marked this with a special ceremony, at the end of which, Solomon got down on his knees in front of all his people and prayed to God. "May God always be with us. May we always obey His commandments."

Then a great feast was held that lasted for seven days.

The Queen of Sheba

1 KINGS 10, 2 CHRONICLES 9

The Queen of Sheba was a curious woman. She had heard of the glorious Temple that Solomon had built for God and how loved he was by his people. She had also heard of his great wisdom.

She thought that Solomon might be able to teach her to be a better Queen, so she decided to make the long journey to Israel. Her arrival caused great excitement. She brought many courtiers and followers with her, and hundreds of camels laden with jewels, gold and spices.

When she was alone with Solomon, she asked his advice on many things. He spent hours with her, patiently answering her questions. The Queen soon realized that Solomon was not only a great King, but also one of the wisest men she had ever met. She showered precious gifts upon him, and Solomon gave her much gold in return.

But for all the gold that Solomon gave her, the Queen knew that he had given her his most precious gift of all . . . wisdom.

The Dividing of Israel

1 KINGS 11

Solomon built many great cities and beautiful buildings while he was King. But all this had to be paid for, so there were many taxes that everyone had to pay. Also, more people were made to work directly for Solomon, rather than on their own land.

Over the years Solomon married many foreign princesses. But these princesses worshiped their own gods. After some time, Solomon began to worship these other gods, too.
"You have not been faithful to me," God told Solomon. "As a punishment, the kingdom of Israel will be taken from your son and divided up."

After Solomon's death, Israel was split in two. Solomon's son, Rehoboam, ruled Judah, in the south of the country, while King Jeroboam ruled the north.

Elijah

1 KINGS 17

After Jeroboam died none of the Kings who followed him were faithful to God. One of them, King Ahab, married a woman called Jezebel. She worshiped a god called Baal, and had many people killed who were loyal to God.

One day, a prophet called Elijah told King Ahab that God had warned him that it would not rain for years, and that many people would starve. Ahab was very angry with Elijah, but God told him to go to the Kerith valley where he would be safe.

Every day, God sent ravens to feed Elijah, and he drank water from a stream. But soon, because there was no rain, the stream dried up. Then God told Elijah to journey to Sidon where a woman would feed him.

When he saw a woman collecting a few sticks to make a fire, Elijah asked her for some food and water. The woman told him that she had only a little flour and a tiny drop of oil left. She was going to make one last loaf of bread for herself and her son before they starved to death.

"Make two small loaves," Elijah told her, "and give one to me. From now on, you will find your flour and oil will never run out."

The woman did as Elijah asked and made him the loaf. Each day afterwards, she found there was just enough flour and oil left to make a loaf of bread with. She and her son never went hungry again.

One day, the woman's son became suddenly ill and died shortly after. The woman was heartbroken.

"Give your son's body to me," Elijah told her. He carried the body to the boy's bed and laid him on it. He then prayed to God three times: "Please, Lord, give this boy his life back."

Suddenly, the boy sat up, alive and well. God had heard Elijah's prayer and answered it. The boy's mother was overcome with joy and fell at Elijah's feet, saying, "You truly are a prophet of God."

The One True God

1 KINGS 18

It still hadn't rained in Israel for many years.
God told Elijah to go back to King Ahab.
"What do you want?" the King asked him angrily.
"Send the prophets and priests of your god, Baal, to meet me at
the top of Mount Carmel."
"And why should I do that?" asked Ahab.
"I want to prove that my God is the one true God," said Elijah.

Ahab agreed to Elijah's test and, on a hot, dry day, sent his priests
and prophets on the long climb to the top of Mount Carmel.
Elijah was waiting for them when they arrived.
He told them to build an altar with the rocks and then to place
a dead bull on top of it.
"Now," said Elijah. "Offer this bull up to your god. Ask him to
send fire down from the sky and set light to it."
The priests and prophets called out to Baal for many hours but
nothing happened.

Then Elijah built his altar and placed a dead bull on it. He then soaked the animal in water and stood back and prayed to God to send fire. Even though the Bull was wet through, it burst into flames.

"Elijah's God is the true God!" everyone cried.

Then Elijah prayed for rain. For the first time in years, the sky grew dark and rain began to fall in Israel.
When King Ahab and his wife, Jezebel, heard what Elijah had done, they vowed to have him killed.
Elijah fled for his life and, after a long and tiring journey, found himself at the foot of Mount Sinai.

"I am so lonely, Lord," he said to God. "I am your only prophet left in Israel. All the others have been killed. Now the King and Jezebel want to kill me, too."
"I know it is dangerous and you are frightened. But you must return," said God. "There is much work to do there."

Daniel and the Lions

DANIEL 1, 6

Many people still disobeyed God's commands, so God allowed the King of Babylon to invade Judah. A lot of people were taken back to Babylon as prisoners. Among them was a small boy called Daniel. He came from a noble family. The King of Babylon wanted children from noble families to be given a good education, so that they would be useful to Babylon in the future.

So Daniel was educated, and treated well while he was growing up, but he never forgot that he was from Judah, and prayed to God three times a day.

When the Persians invaded Babylon, their King, Darius, began to rule the country. By this time, Daniel had grown up and was famous for being a wise and popular man. King Darius liked Daniel so much he made him one of the three rulers of the whole country. But the other two rulers were jealous of Daniel and wanted to be rid of him.

Knowing that Daniel still prayed three times a day to God, the other two rulers made a new law. This law said that for the next thirty days, people should only pray to King Darius. If anyone broke this law they would be fed to the lions. So the jealous rulers went to Darius and told him that Daniel was still praying to God, and therefore, Daniel must die.

As much as Darius liked Daniel, he knew he could not save him. The very next day Daniel was thrown into the lions' pit and a large rock was pushed over the opening. That night, Darius was so worried for Daniel that he could not sleep.

Early the next morning, Darius rushed to the lions' pit and had the rock pushed back.

"Are you still alive, my friend?" he shouted into the pit, fearing the worst.

"I am!" cried Daniel. "My God knew I had done you no wrong and has kept me alive!"

Darius was overcome with joy to see Daniel alive and well. He had him brought out of the pit and had the two jealous rulers thrown in there, instead. The lions showed them no mercy and killed them at once.

"Let everyone in my kingdom respect and fear Daniel's God," King Darius decreed. "For he is the one and only true God."

Jonah and the Whale

JONAH 1-4

Another of God's prophets was called Jonah. God sent Jonah to the city of Nineveh to warn the people that God was angry with them because they were not obeying His laws. But instead of following God's command, Jonah ran away to the port of Joppa. He boarded a boat that was sailing to Tarshish, which was a long way from Nineveh.

When the boat was far out at sea, it started to rain. The wind became stronger and the waves became higher. Soon, the boat was being tossed around in a huge storm. The captain was so afraid they might sink, he ordered the sailors to throw things overboard to make the boat lighter. Then he rushed below deck to wake Jonah, who was fast asleep.

"Pray to your God to save us!" cried the captain. "Otherwise we will all die!"

"I can't pray to Him," said Jonah. "I'm running away from Him!" The sailors begged Jonah to pray to God to make the storm die down. "The storm will only die down if you throw me into the sea," said Jonah. The sailors did not want to do this, but the storm was getting worse, so they reluctantly agreed. With heavy hearts, they lifted Jonah up and threw him overboard. As soon as they had done so, the storm suddenly died down. The sailors got down on their knees and thanked Jonah's God for saving their lives.

Jonah thought he would surely die, but just as he was sinking beneath the waves, a whale swam by and swallowed him whole. Jonah lived in the whale for three days. At the end of the three days, the whale opened its great mouth and spat him out onto dry land. Jonah had been saved.

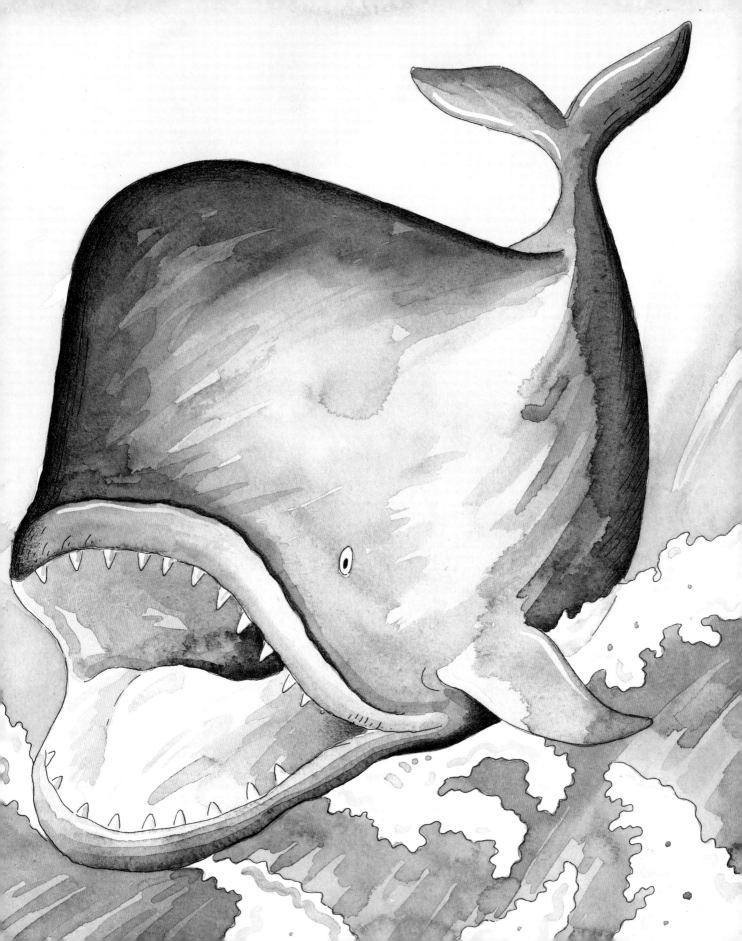

Then God spoke to Jonah again.

"I have saved your life. Do not disobey me again. Go to the city of Nineveh and tell the people that I will destroy them at the end of forty days if they do not change their ways."

This time Jonah did as he was told. When he told the King in Nineveh of God's warning, the King ordered his people to begin praying to God again.

Jonah sat outside the city gates waiting to see if God would destroy the city or not. God made a vine grow to keep Jonah in the shade and protect him from the fierce sun. But the next day a worm came and ate the vine away. Once again, the sun beat down on him and Jonah became angry.

"Let this be a lesson for you, Jonah," said God. "Just as you cared about the vine that grew up overnight and then was gone, so I care about the people of Nineveh who went away from me. Should I not love them, Jonah, as I love you?"

The King Will Come

MICAH 5

There were many times that God's people disobeyed Him. Sometimes they lost their faith that He was the only true God, and were tempted to worship other gods. But the prophets knew God only wanted peace for His people and that He had great plans for their future.

They knew that one day, a new King of Israel would be born in the little town of Bethlehem. He would be God's own son and he would spread God's laws throughout the whole world.

This new King would be called Jesus, and his story is told in the New Testament.

119

THE NEW TESTAMENT

Mary's Message

LUKE 1

Many years ago there lived a young girl called Mary. She was born in a village called Nazareth which was tucked away in the hills of Galilee.

Mary was very happy. She was engaged to be married to a carpenter called Joseph who also lived in the village.

One evening, as Mary sat quietly in her room, a blinding light suddenly appeared. She put her hand up to her face to shield her eyes but, through her fingers, Mary could dimly make out a shimmering figure in the very centre of the light.

"Don't be afraid, Mary," said the figure. "I am Gabriel, an angel of God. I have come to give you a message."
The angel's voice was so beautiful that Mary lost all her fear.
"What message do you have for me?" she asked, calmly.
"I have come to tell you that you are going to have a baby," replied Gabriel.

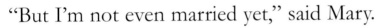

"But I'm not even married yet," said Mary.

"The Holy Spirit will come down and God's power will rest upon you," said Gabriel. "You will have a baby and you must call him Jesus. And he will be the Son of God."

"I am God's servant," Mary said quietly. "God's wish is my desire."

She raised her head, only to find herself in an empty room.

The angel Gabriel had left as silently as he had come.

Joseph the Carpenter

MATTHEW 1

Joseph the carpenter was an honest man. On hearing that his bride to be, Mary, was expecting a baby, he became very sad. "I am not the father of this child," he thought. "Therefore, I cannot marry her."

Being a good, caring man he decided to break off his engagement to Mary in private, so fewer people would know of her shame.

But one night he had a strange dream. In his dream, an angel of God appeared and said to him:
"Do not break with Mary. She has done nothing wrong. The child she is carrying is the Son of God. You will name the baby Jesus. He will grow up to save the world from its sins."

When Joseph woke up, he thought about the dream. He realized that his dream was not a dream at all. It was a message from God. With a happy heart he began to make preparations to marry Mary as soon as possible.

The Birth of Jesus

LUKE 2

Mary and Joseph were married. They loved each other very much and were looking forward to the birth of their baby.

The happy couple started to prepare their home in Nazareth for the birth. Then they heard some news that would change everything: The Roman Emperor, Augustus, who ruled the land, had made a new law. The new law said that everyone who was not living in their place of birth had to return there to register for a new tax. Joseph was born in Bethlehem, so he and Mary had to go there straight away.

Joseph and Mary hurried, because the baby was due to be born very soon. They quickly gathered together some clothes, a few warm blankets and some food and water for the journey. They packed it all on their donkey and started out on the road to Bethlehem.

It was nightfall by the time they arrived, tired and hungry. Even worse, all the inns where they could have stayed were full. After searching for some hours, the only place where they could find shelter was an empty stable.

Joseph made the stable as comfortable as he could for his wife, who laid down to rest. Some time later, Mary gave birth to a little baby boy. She gave thanks for his safe delivery and called him Jesus, as the angel Gabriel had asked her to.

On the Hillside

LUKE 2

On the night the infant Jesus was born, some shepherds were guarding their sheep in the hills above Bethlehem. All of a sudden, a great light filled the sky and an angel appeared before them. The shepherds were very afraid.

"Do not be afraid," said the angel. "The Son of God has been born tonight. His name is Jesus. Go into the town and worship him. You will find him lying in a manger in a stable."

Then the whole sky filled with angels, and they were singing: "Glory to God in the highest, and peace on Earth to all the people who love Him."

The shepherds rushed down the hills and into the town. They soon found the stable where Mary and Joseph were caring for the baby Jesus. They knelt before him and stared in wonder at their new Lord.

When they left the stable, the shepherds walked excitedly through the streets of Bethlehem. They told everyone they met of the angel's visit, and how everything the angel told them had come true.

That night, they walked back into the hills to find their sheep. They talked happily amongst themselves and sang praises to God. Sleeping under the stars, they dreamed of their new King.

Three Wise Men

MATTHEW 2

One night, in a country far from Bethlehem, three wise men were riding their camels along a dusty road when they noticed a new star in the sky. It seemed to shine brighter than all the rest. "This star is a sign," they said. "It means a new King has been born. We must follow the star and it will lead us to him."

The star led them to the city of Jerusalem where King Herod ruled. Herod had already heard of the birth of a special baby in Bethlehem. He had learned from his priests that the baby would grow up to be the King of the Jews. Herod was angry and jealous. He didn't want to lose his power, especially to a baby born in a lowly stable.

He asked to meet the three wise men.
"I hear you are going to Bethlehem to worship a baby who will grow up to be King," he said. "Please tell me exactly where you find him, so I may go and worship him too."
The three wise men agreed, and the next morning they set out on the road to Bethlehem.

That night they arrived at the stable. When they saw the baby Jesus, they knelt down in front of him and offered him gifts. They had brought gold, sweet frankincense and myrrh. After they had blessed the child, the three wise men went quietly away and camped in the hills outside Bethlehem.

The wise men had planned to go back to Jerusalem the next morning and tell King Herod where to find the baby Jesus.

But that night they had a dream. In the dream, an angel told them that if they told Herod where to find the baby boy, Herod would kill him. As dawn broke, they quickly packed their belongings onto their camels, and took a different road back to their own country. The road took them away from Herod.

At the same time, Joseph also had a dream. In it, an angel told him the baby Jesus was in great danger. When he woke, Joseph told Mary of his dream. A worried Mary said they should leave at once. Joseph hurriedly loaded their donkey while Mary wrapped the sleeping Jesus in warm blankets. Then they started out on a long long journey to a country called Egypt.

Joseph, Mary and Jesus lived in Egypt until King Herod died.
Now that they were not in danger, they decided
it was safe to return to Nazareth.
At long last, they were going home.

139

The Boy Jesus

LUKE 2

Jesus was brought up in Nazareth and grew to be a strong and healthy boy. When he was twelve years old, Joseph and Mary decided he was old enough to travel to Jerusalem with them to celebrate the great feast of the Passover.

The journey took many days. When they arrived in Jerusalem, the streets were already full of people who had come from all over the country to celebrate Passover.

When the feast was over Mary and Joseph walked alongside the many people who were journeying back to Nazareth. Although they couldn't see Jesus, Mary and Joseph thought he must be with a group of children who were walking together.

When it became dark, everyone stopped to make camp. Joseph laid blankets on the ground, while Mary set out some food. But when they called for Jesus he didn't answer. They called again . . . there was still no reply. They searched all over the camp but Jesus was nowhere to be seen. They realized they must have left him behind in the city. A worried Joseph and Mary hurriedly packed their blankets and started back on the road to Jerusalem.

They searched for Jesus in Jerusalem for three days and nights.

Finally, they found him sitting in the Temple talking with the teachers. They were amazed to see Jesus was not only listening carefully to the teachers, but also asking questions that an ordinary twelve year old would not think of.

"Where have you been?" asked Mary, relieved to see him again. "We have been searching everywhere for you."
"I'm sorry I worried you," replied Jesus, calmly. "But I thought you would know I'd be in my Father's house. I'll always be safe here."

Happy that he had come to no harm, Mary and Joseph forgave him, and they all started the long journey back to Nazareth.

The Baptism of Jesus

MATTHEW 3, MARK 1, LUKE 3, JOHN 1

Mary had a cousin called Elizabeth, who had a son called John. John grew up to be a strong, healthy man who was devoted to God. Many people went to Galilee to hear him speak. He would tell them to always share their food and clothes with poor people who had few belongings of their own.

John would baptize the people who believed in God. He would take them to the nearby river Jordan and carefully pour a little water over their heads. This meant these people had been washed clean of their sins, and from that day on could start to lead new, good lives. John told his followers that one day a man would make himself known to them all.

"This man will be the true Lord," he said.

When Jesus was thirty years old he waved goodbye to Joseph and Mary and left Nazareth. He went to Galilee to seek out his cousin, John. Jesus had heard that John was teaching God's message, and wanted to be baptized by him.

As soon as John saw him, he recognized Jesus for being the true Son of God.

"I am not worthy to baptize you," he told Jesus. "It is you who should baptize me."

"Let us do God's will," replied Jesus, and walked into the river until the water was up to his waist.

John followed and, scooping up a little water in his hand, gently baptized Jesus. All of a sudden the sky opened and a white dove, who was the spirit of God, flew down and hovered over Jesus's head. Then God's voice rang out, saying:

"This is my dear Son and I am pleased with him."

The First Miracle

JOHN 2

One day, Jesus was invited to a wedding. The marriage was to take place in Galilee, in a town called Cana. Jesus's mother, Mary, was invited too.

Everyone enjoyed themselves but, half way through the wedding feast, the wine ran out.

"What are we to do?" asked the Master of the Feast. "How can we enjoy the rest of our food without wine?"

Mary overheard the worried man and thought Jesus might be able to do something about it. She whispered into her son's ear. "Can you help? This poor man has run out of wine to offer his guests."

"Do not ask me this," Jesus replied anxiously. "My time has not yet come."

But Mary was already turning to the servants, saying, "Do whatever he tells you to do."

Not wishing to disobey his mother, Jesus decided to help.

Nearby lay six empty water jars, from which the wedding guests had washed their hands before eating. Jesus told the servants to refill all six of the jars with water.

"Now," he said, "pour a little of the water into a cup and take it to the Master of the Feast."

The servants did as they were told.

When the Master of the Feast tasted the water, it had miraculously turned into wine.

"What wonderful wine! What a clever man you are!" he exclaimed, slapping the bridegroom on the back. "Everyone else serves the best wine first and keeps the cheapest until last. But you have saved the best until last!"

Only the servants who served the wine knew of Jesus's powers. This was the first miracle that Jesus ever performed.

Twelve Disciples

MARK 1, 3, LUKE 5, 6

Jesus was becoming famous throughout the land. Wherever he went, people flocked around to hear him speak of God. One day, he was speaking on the shores of the Sea of Galilee and, as usual, there was a large crowd pressing in on him so that they could hear every word.

Jesus was getting closer and closer to the water's edge. When he saw a fishing boat nearby, he asked the fishermen if they would take him a little way out to sea so the crowds could see him better. The fishermen were Andrew and his brother, Peter.

After he had finished speaking to the crowds, Jesus told Andrew and Peter to row out to deeper waters and cast their net.
"We've been fishing all night," they complained, "and we haven't even caught one fish!"
"Do as I tell you and you will be rewarded," Jesus replied.

152

The fishermen did as Jesus asked. When they hauled in their net, they were amazed to see it was so full of fish it was almost bursting! They called to their friends, James and John, who were fishing nearby, to help them take all the fish back to shore.

The fishermen were pleased with their catch but were frightened of Jesus's powers.

"Do not be scared," said Jesus, gently. "Come with me and I will make you fishers of men."

Andrew, Peter, James and John left their boats that day and followed Jesus wherever he went. They became his first disciples.

As Jesus journeyed through the country, preaching the word of God, he collected more disciples along the way. Soon there were twelve of them. Apart from the four fishermen of Galilee, there was Philip, Matthew, Thomas, Bartholomew, another James, Judas, Simon and Judas Iscariot. They all loved Jesus, and they, too, became messengers of God.

The Sermon on the Mount

MATTHEW 5-7, LUKE 6

When Jesus taught on Sundays, the Sabbath, he often taught indoors, in a temple. On other days, he liked to speak outside, where the air was fresh and clear. Sometimes, there was a breeze to help cool down the hot, sunny days.

One day, Jesus climbed to the top of a small mountain. Many people followed to hear him speak.

Jesus told them if they obeyed God, that God would look after them. He told them not to be greedy, and not to want more money and possessions than they really needed. He told them they should try to love their enemies as well as their friends. He also told them to treat other people as they would want to be treated themselves. "If you do all this," he said. "God will see you and reward you."

He told them to pray, and taught them a prayer so they could speak to God whenever they needed to:

Our Father who is in Heaven,
hallowed be Thy name.
Your kingdom come,
Your will be done,
on Earth as it is in Heaven.
Give us this day our daily bread,
and forgive us the wrongs we have done,
as we forgive those who do wrong to us.
Lead us not into temptation,
and deliver us from evil.

Amen.

Jesus Heals the Sick

MATTHEW 8, LUKE 7, 18

As Jesus's fame grew and grew, more people flocked to his side, hoping to catch a glimpse of him. The ill and diseased fought their way through the crowds, hoping that Jesus would heal them.

One day a blind beggar, unable to push his way to Jesus's side, shouted out:

"Son of David, have mercy on me!"

Jesus heard the blind man's call and asked that he be brought to him.

"What do you want from me?" Jesus asked.

"Lord, let me see!" pleaded the beggar.

Jesus laid his hands on the man's head, and said:

"Receive your sight. Your faith has healed you."

When Jesus took his hands away, the beggar could see again.

Another time, Jesus was asked to visit the house of a Roman soldier. The soldier's servant was very ill and close to death. As Jesus neared his house, the soldier rushed out to meet him.

"Lord, although I am not worthy to have you enter my home, please say a prayer so my servant will be healed."

Jesus was surprised and moved by the strength of the soldier's belief in him.

"I have not seen faith as strong as this in the whole of Israel," he said.

After Jesus had left him, the soldier went back into his house and found his servant completely cured of his illness.

A Terrible Storm

MATTHEW 14, MARK 6, JOHN 6

After Jesus had finished speaking one afternoon, he told his disciples to sail home in their boats. He told them he wanted to go into the hills and pray, and he would meet with them later.

But as the disciples made their way out to sea, the wind grew strong and it began to rain. The further they sailed from the shore, the worse the weather became. The wind howled, the driving rain lashed at their faces and huge waves rolled and crashed around them.

The disciples became very afraid. They didn't know if they were going to keep the boat from sinking. The worst thing of all was that it would soon be dark.

It took all the disciples' strength to keep the little boat afloat. They worked hard all night knowing that they would surely drown if they failed.

As the sun started to rise, the disciples were very weary from all their efforts.

Suddenly, they all cried out in terror, when out of the early morning mist, a ghostly figure appeared to be walking on the water towards them. But the figure calmed them, simply saying:

"Do not be afraid. It is I, Jesus."

Peter could not believe his eyes and shouted out:

"If it is really you, Lord. Command me to walk on the water as well!" Jesus held out his hand. "Come," he said.

Peter scrambled over the side of the boat and tried to walk on the water too, but courage failed him and he began to sink.

"Lord, save me!" he shouted.

Jesus grasped his hand tightly, and helped him back to the safety of the small boat.

"Peter," said Jesus gently. "How little your faith is. Why did you doubt me?"

Peter asked for Jesus's forgiveness, and then he and the other disciples knelt down in front of him.

"You really are the Son of God," they said.

163

The Good Shepherd

MATTHEW 18, LUKE 15, JOHN 10

Jesus often told people stories, so they could understand more easily what he was trying to teach them.

All sorts of people came to listen to Jesus. Some of them had done bad things in their lives. Many teachers of God's Word thought that Jesus should not be speaking with people who had done wrong. But Jesus thought that everyone should have the chance to be forgiven. He told this simple story to make them understand:

165

"If a shepherd has a hundred sheep," said Jesus, "and one sheep takes a wrong path and gets lost, what does the shepherd do? He makes sure the other ninety-nine sheep are safe and then looks for the one missing sheep. He does not stop looking until he finds it. Then the shepherd will ask his friends and family to celebrate with him the return of the lost sheep.

"It is the same for people," Jesus continued. "When they get lost and stray from the path to God, they sometimes do bad things. But there is joy in Heaven when they find the path that leads them to God again.

"I am like that shepherd," said Jesus. "I help people who have strayed from the path to God, and I lead them to Him again. People are like my sheep. I will always protect them. I love them, and I would die for them."

Seeds that Fall

MATTHEW 13, MARK 4, LUKE 8

Jesus used to tell another story to make people understand God's message. It was about a man who sowed seed.

"One day a man went out with a bag of seed to sow," began Jesus. "Some of the seed he threw fell on a stony path, where birds flew down and ate it.

"Some of the seed fell on rough, rocky ground where there was hardly any soil. When the corn began to sprout into young plants, the strong sun dried them up and they died.

"Some of the seed fell amongst weeds. As the young corn plants tried to grow, the weeds wrapped themselves around the plants and choked them.

"But some seed fell on good ground. The young plants grew well and produced much corn."
Jesus then explained this story to his followers.

"Some people are like the seed which fell on the stony path; they hear God's message but choose not to believe it.

"Other people are like the seed that fell on the rough, stony ground; they, too, hear God's message but, when life becomes hard, they choose not to obey it.

"And some people are like the seed that fell amongst the weeds; they let their love of money and possessions blind them to God's message.

"But for people who are like the seed that fell on the good ground, they are blessed. They have heard God's message. They understand that God's Word is the truth, and they try every day to obey His laws."

The Tax Collector

LUKE 19

At one time, Jesus was passing through the city of Jericho. A rich tax collector called Zacchaeus lived near to where Jesus was passing. Being a small man, Zacchaeus climbed a tree to get a better view of Jesus as he went by. When Jesus spotted Zacchaeus in the branches, he told him to climb down.

"May I stay at your house, tonight?" Jesus asked him.

Many people thought it wrong of their Lord to stay in the house of a man who collected money and was sometimes known to cheat. But Jesus knew it was the right thing to do. Zacchaeus's meeting with Jesus changed the tax collector forever. To everyone's surprise, Zacchaeus decided to give half of his money to the poor. He also offered to repay four times the amount of money he had wrongly taken from people.

Jesus turned to his followers and said: "Salvation has come to this man, Zacchaeus, today. The Son of Man seeks out and saves those who are lost."

Jairus's Daughter

MATTHEW 9, MARK 5, LUKE 8

There was once a man called Jairus who was the leader of a synagogue. One day, while Jesus was preaching, Jairus pushed his way through the crowds to see him.

"Help me, Master," he said. "My little daughter is very ill. I'm afraid she's going to die. Please come to my house and see her."

Jesus agreed at once. He and Jairus began to make their way through the throngs of people that now followed Jesus everywhere.

When a woman touched Jesus's robe as he passed by, Jesus turned
and asked, "Who touched me?"
The woman stepped forward.
"I did, Master. I have been ill for many years. Now that I have
touched your robe, I am healed."
"Your faith has made you well," said Jesus. "Go in peace."

A messenger from Jairus's house was sent out to meet them.
"I have bad news for you, Jairus," he said. "Your daughter has died."
Jairus fell to the ground with grief.

At Jairus's house, many people were standing outside weeping. Jesus comforted them.

"The girl is not dead. She is just sleeping," he said.

Jesus went to the girl's side and took her hand.

"Get up, my child," he said, softly.

The girl slowly opened her eyes and then climbed out of bed as Jesus had commanded. She was completely cured.

Feeding the Five Thousand

MATTHEW 14, MARK 6, LUKE 9, JOHN 6

One day, Jesus was speaking on a hillside near to the shores of Lake Galilee. Over five thousand people had come to hear his words. By the evening everyone was still there, listening intently to what he had to say.

One of his disciples rushed up to him.

"Lord, these people have been here all day with nothing to eat. They must be very hungry, and all I can find is a small boy who has five loaves of bread and two fishes."

"Bring him to me," said Jesus.

When the boy arrived, Jesus took the basket of loaves and fishes from him and bowed his head in prayer.

Jesus then began to walk among the people, handing out the food.

Magically, the small basket of loaves and fishes never seemed to run out. Eventually, all five thousand people had been fed until they could eat no more. There was even enough food left over to fill twelve large baskets.

The Good Samaritan

LUKE 10

"What does 'love thy neighbor' mean?" someone once asked Jesus.

"Listen," said Jesus, "and I will tell you."

Then Jesus told this story:

"There was once a man who was on his way from Jerusalem to Jericho. On a lonely stretch of the road, some thieves set upon him. They hit him and kicked him many times, and took all his money.

Later, a priest happened to pass by. He took one look at the man lying at the side of the road and, pretending not to see him, passed by without helping him.

Not long after, another priest passed by. He, too, couldn't be bothered to help the poor man, and just kept on walking.

A few hours later, another man passed by. This man was a Samaritan. Samaritans and Jews did not like one another. But this Samaritan was kind. He comforted the man, let him drink from his water bottle and bandaged his wounds. Then he helped him onto his donkey and took him to a nearby inn where the man could rest. 'Here's some money,' he said to the innkeeper. 'Please let this man stay until he is well. If I owe you any more, I will pay you next time I am passing through.'"

When Jesus finished his story, he said to everyone listening:
"The Samaritans and the Jews hated each other, yet it was a
Samaritan who helped the Jew when he most needed it. This is what
I mean when I tell you to 'love thy neighbor'.
No matter how different a person may be from you, we are all
God's children, and we should be kind to everyone."

Jesus Raises the Dead

LUKE 10, JOHN 11

When Jesus was in Jerusalem, he often stayed with his friends, Mary, Martha and their brother, Lazarus.

Once, while Jesus was teaching outside the city, Mary sent a message to him telling him that her brother, Lazarus, was very ill. She wanted Jesus to go to Lazarus and make him well again.

But, when Jesus arrived two days later, Lazarus had already died. "Lord, if you had arrived earlier, my brother would still be alive!" Martha cried.

"Lazarus will live again," said Jesus. "Take me to him."

Lazarus's body had been placed in a large cave, and a huge rock had been put in front of its entrance.

Jesus asked that the rock be moved away.

When the rock had been moved, all was quiet except for a light breeze rattling the leaves in the trees.

Then Jesus spoke:

"Lazarus, come out!" he commanded.

Everyone gasped, when Lazarus stumbled out of the tomb, still wrapped in his grave clothes.

"Our brother is alive!" wept Mary and Martha, who got down on their knees and gave their thanks to God.

This was one of Jesus's greatest miracles. After hearing of the raising of Lazarus, many more people realized that Jesus was the true Son of God. But there were other people who were afraid of Jesus's powers and wanted to destroy him. Jesus knew that his time on Earth would be short and, that eventually, he would suffer and die.

The Prodigal Son

LUKE 15

Jesus never turned people away who had come to hear him speak, even if they had done many bad things in their lives. "God will always forgive those who want to learn to be good," he said.

To teach people about forgiveness, he often told this story:

"There was once a wealthy farmer who had two sons. The eldest son worked hard on his father's farm all day, while the youngest son was selfish and lazy. One day, the selfish son said to his father, 'I know that my brother and I will get all your money when you die, but I'd like my share now.'"

Because his father loved him, he agreed to give his youngest son half his wealth.

187

As soon as he'd received the money, the youngest son went to live in a different country. He had a grand house and wore the most expensive clothes. He made many new friends, and often held magnificent parties which overflowed with the finest food and wines.

But, after a while, his money ran out. He lost his house and his fine clothes. When his friends realized he had no money left, they stopped seeing him too. He was so poor, he started to beg for food from people in the streets. After a while, he managed to get a job looking after some pigs. But the job was so badly paid he was often hungry and was even tempted to eat the filthy swill the pigs ate. "My father's servants live better than I do," he thought. "I will return home and beg my father's forgiveness."

When he arrived at the farm, his father rushed out to greet him. "My boy, my boy, you have returned!" he said, excitedly. "I am so happy to see you again."

That night he arranged a huge party to celebrate his son's return.

When the eldest son came home that evening from a hard day's work in the fields, he heard the sound of music and laughter coming from inside the house.

"What's happening?" he asked a servant.

"Do not you know?" replied the servant. "Your brother has come home and your father has invited all his friends to welcome his return."

The eldest son became very upset when he heard this and stormed into the house.

"Why are you doing this for him?" he asked his father, angrily. "He took your money and has wasted it all, while I stayed with you and worked hard on your farm. In all that time you have never invited my friends here and given a party for me."

"Oh, my son," said his father, putting a comforting arm around his eldest son's shoulders. "Do you not know that I love you more than life itself? But you must try and understand; your brother was lost to me, and now he is found."

The Paralyzed Man

MATTHEW 9, MARK 2, LUKE 5

Once, Jesus was teaching inside someone's house. As usual, there were hundreds of people who wanted to get close to him and hear what he was saying. The house quickly filled up with many people, and there were lots more outside, crowding around the door and windows hoping to get a glimpse of him.

Suddenly, four men approached the house. They were carrying their friend on a bed mat. He had suffered a terrible disease that had left him paralyzed. His friends were taking him to see Jesus, whom they hoped would help. But, there were so many people crowding around the door, it was impossible to get through.

One of the men had an idea.
"Why don't we cut a hole in the roof," he said. "It's only made of straw. Then we can lower our friend into the room where Jesus is."

The others agreed and, soon, the paralyzed man was lying at Jesus's feet.

When Jesus saw what the men had done, he was moved by the care they had shown their friend.

He knelt down by the paralyzed man and took his hand.
"Your sins are forgiven. Now stand, pick up your mat and go home."
The man did as Jesus told him to do. He was completely cured, and everyone who saw the miracle was amazed.

Entering Jerusalem

MATTHEW 21, MARK 11 LUKE 19, JOHN 12

Although Jesus knew his time on earth was coming to an end, he and his disciples decided to go to Jerusalem to celebrate the feast of the Passover. Jesus rode on the back of a donkey as he entered the city. People lined the road to see him. It was as if a king had come. They threw their shawls down in front of him and cut down palm leaves to lay in his path.

When Jesus arrived at the Temple he became very angry. Instead of people praying, the Temple was full of people making money by buying and selling things. Jesus was so upset, he overturned their tables and drove everyone out, shouting after them:

"This house should be a house of prayer, but you have turned it into a den of thieves!"

The Temple leaders were shocked by Jesus's behaviour. They feared that Jesus was becoming too powerful. They wanted to get rid of him. Soon, they would have their chance.

The Betrayal of Jesus

MATTHEW 26, MARK 14, LUKE 22

One of Jesus's disciples was called Judas Iscariot. Judas had started to believe that Jesus was not who he said he was, that he was not the true Son of God. These thoughts made Judas do something terrible.

One afternoon, while the rest of the disciples were buying food in the market for the feast of the Passover, Judas secretly sneaked away to meet the Temple priests. He knew that the priests were not pleased with Jesus and wanted to be rid of him.

"I am with Jesus all the time," he whispered to them. "I can tell you where you can arrest him quietly, away from the crowds."
"How much do you want for this information?" the priests asked him.
"Thirty pieces of silver," replied Judas.
The Temple priests gave him the money and, when he'd left, smiled contentedly together.
"Soon, Jesus will be ours!" they said.

The Last Supper

MATTHEW 26, MARK 14, LUKE 22, JOHN 13

Peter and John, two of Jesus's disciples, asked Jesus where they were going to eat the feast of the Passover.

"Follow a man who is carrying a jar of water. He will lead you to his house. We will have our feast there," Jesus told them.

Later, Jesus and all the disciples gathered in an upstairs room in the house to celebrate the Passover. Then Jesus did a strange thing: he knelt down and washed the feet of each of his disciples.

"You should not be doing this, Master," the disciples protested. "You are our Lord and Teacher."

"I am your Lord and Teacher," Jesus replied. "And you must remember to serve each other in the same way that I have just served you."

"My time in this world has almost come to an end," he continued.

"Tonight, one of you will betray me."

The disciples became angry when they heard this.

"Who, Lord? Which one of us could do such a thing?" they cried.

"The one I pass this bread to," said Jesus.

He broke off some bread and passed it to Judas, saying to him:

"Go, do what you have to do."

Judas stood up, hung his head in shame and left the room, walking quickly into the dark night.

After Judas had left, Jesus broke up the rest of the bread and passed it to each of the disciples.

"Eat this bread which is my body, and remember me," he told them. Then he lifted up a cup of wine.

"Drink this wine which is my blood," he said, "and remember me." Everyone was sad. They prayed and sang a hymn together, before leaving the room.

The Garden of Gethsemane

MATTHEW 26, MARK 14, LUKE 22, JOHN 18

Jesus and his disciples walked up the Mount of Olives and into the Garden of Gethsemane.

On the way, Jesus told Peter that Peter would deny knowing him three times later that night.

"I would never say I didn't know you," said Peter. "I love you, Lord. I would rather die than pretend I didn't know you."

"We shall see," replied Jesus.

Jesus asked Peter, James and John to enter the garden with him. The rest of the disciples kept guard near the garden's gates. He left Peter, James and John after a while and walked further into the garden by himself so he could be alone to pray.

"I am scared, Father," he prayed to God. "I do not wish to die, but if it is Your will, then so be it."

When he returned, he found that Peter, James and John had fallen asleep.

"Could you not stay awake for even one hour?" he asked them, and then left them to pray again.

When he returned, they had fallen asleep again. This happened for a third time, after which, the disciples were woken up by shouting at the gates, and by torches that lit up the sky.

It was the priests from the Temple with the Temple guards. They were being led by Judas, and had come to take Jesus away. Judas walked straight up to Jesus and kissed him.

"This is he," said Judas, turning to the soldiers, who grabbed Jesus roughly by the arms. Peter was so angry at the way they were treating Jesus, he drew his sword and cut an ear off one of the priest's servants.

"Put your sword away, Peter," said Jesus, quietly. He touched the servant's ear and made it whole again.

Then the soldiers led Jesus out of the garden. The disciples were so frightened, they ran away.

Later that night, Peter was asked three times if he was a friend of Jesus. Peter denied knowing him each time he was asked. When he realized what he had said, he leaned against a tree and wept.

Jesus on Trial

MATTHEW 27, MARK 15, LUKE 23, JOHN 18-19

The priests of the Temple had decided that Jesus must die, but they were not allowed to put anyone to death. So they had Jesus dragged in front of the Roman governor, Pontius Pilate. He was a powerful man who had the authority to order an execution.

"What has he done wrong?" Pilate asked the priests.
"He says he is a king," they replied.
"Are you the King of the Jews?" Pilate asked Jesus.
"You say I am," said Jesus and, bowing his head, refused to answer any more questions.

Pilate thought Jesus was innocent and asked the crowd:
"This man has done nothing wrong. What would you have me do with him?"
"Crucify him!" the crowd yelled back.

Under Roman law, Pilate had the power to set one prisoner free during Passover.

"Whom shall I set free?" he asked the crowd. "This man Jesus or this common murderer, Barabbas?"

"Set Barabbas free," they shouted. "Crucify Jesus!"

"Very well," he said. "You shall have your way. Barabbas will be set free, but Jesus will be crucified!"

Carrying the Cross

MATTHEW 27, MARK 15, LUKE 23, JOHN 18-19

Jesus was handed over to some Roman soldiers who beat and whipped him until he was very weak. As he lay on the ground bleeding, the soldiers began to laugh at him and mock him.

"Oh, Your Majesty," said one of them. "I've made a special crown for you."

And he put a crown made of thorns on Jesus's head.

"Here's your royal robe," jeered another soldier, putting an old purple shawl around Jesus's shoulders.

Then it was time for Jesus to carry the cross, on which he would be nailed, to the place of crucifixions. He stumbled through the streets bearing the heavy, wooden cross on his back. Behind him, the Roman soldiers were taunting him and whipping him on.

After a while, Jesus did not have the strength to stand. So the soldiers told a man they saw in the crowd to help Jesus carry the cross. This man's name was Simon.

Finally, they reached the place where Jesus was to be crucified. It lay just outside the city and was called Golgotha.

The Crucifixion

MATTHEW 27, MARK 15, LUKE 23, JOHN 18-19

Then the soldiers ripped Jesus's clothes from him and laid him on the cross while it was still on the ground. They nailed his hands and feet to the cross, and put a sign on it which said: 'Jesus of Nazareth. King of The Jews'. Then they raised the cross, and set it in the ground between two thieves, who were also being crucified.

People in the crowd jeered at Jesus.
"Save yourself if you are truly the Son of God," they shouted.
But Jesus said nothing. His mother, Mary, was standing with John, one of Jesus's disciples. She wept at her son's suffering.
"Look after my mother as if you were her own son," said Jesus looking down at John.

At midday, the sky suddenly went dark and stayed that way for three hours. Jesus cried out: "My God! My God! Why have you forgotten me?"

A little while later, he asked for some water to help his thirst. A cruel soldier gave him a sponge, soaked in vinegar, to drink from.

Shortly after, Jesus gave a terrible cry, then whispered, "It is finished." Then he closed his eyes and died. At that moment, the ground shook and the curtain in the Temple ripped from top to bottom.
One Roman soldier looked up wide-eyed with wonder at Jesus's body on the cross.
"Truly," he said. "This man was the Son of God."

217

The Empty Tomb

MATTHEW 27-28, MARK 15-16, LUKE 23-24, JOHN 19-20

After Jesus's body was taken down from the cross, it was wrapped in a sheet and taken to a cave which would serve as Jesus's tomb. A large rock was laid across its entrance.

Three days later, Mary Magdalene went with a friend to pray outside the tomb. To the women's amazement, they found that the rock had been rolled away from the entrance. When they looked inside, they saw that Jesus's body was gone. All that was left inside was the sheet that he had been wrapped in.

Two of the disciples, Peter and John, were sent for. They too were puzzled as to what had happened. John became scared and didn't want to go into the tomb. Peter thought the body might have been stolen, but secretly hoped that Jesus had risen from the dead.

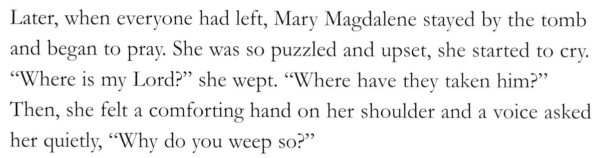

Later, when everyone had left, Mary Magdalene stayed by the tomb and began to pray. She was so puzzled and upset, she started to cry. "Where is my Lord?" she wept. "Where have they taken him?"

Then, she felt a comforting hand on her shoulder and a voice asked her quietly, "Why do you weep so?"

"Because they have taken my Lord away," she replied.

"Mary, do you not know me?" said the voice, softly. "It is I."

Mary turned around and was astonished to see Jesus standing by her side.

"Do not be afraid," Jesus said. "For soon, I will be with my Father in Heaven. Go now, and tell the others that you have seen me."

Full of joy, Mary rushed to tell the disciples that she had seen Jesus and spoken with him.

Jesus and Peter

JOHN 21

Shortly after Jesus had risen from the tomb, Peter was out fishing on the Sea of Galilee. He and some other disciples had been fishing all night, but had not caught a single fish.

All of a sudden a man shouted at them from the shore, "Throw your net over the right side of the boat."
Nobody recognized that the man was Jesus. They did as they were told, and when they pulled up the net, it was full of fish.

"Only Jesus could have done this," said one of the disciples.

Peter was so excited to see Jesus again he swam to the shore to greet him. By the time the others caught up, Jesus had already lit a fire.

"Let us cook some of the fish you caught," he said.

After eating, Jesus asked Peter if he loved him.

"You know I do," replied Peter.

Jesus asked him the question twice more. Each time Peter gave the same reply: "You know I do."

Jesus smiled and, hugging Peter, told him he should always care for the other disciples.

The Last Word

ACTS 1

The last time the disciples saw Jesus was on the Mount of Olives. He had come to say goodbye to them.

"You must speak bravely and honestly about me," said Jesus. "You must spread God's teachings to the furthest parts of this country, and to people from other countries, too. In this way the Word of God and His love will spread throughout the whole world."

Then a mist came down and covered Jesus so that the disciples could not see him anymore. When the mist cleared, Jesus had disappeared. He had been taken to Heaven to be with his Father, Almighty God, and to sit by His side forever.